TEN IN A BED

Mary Rees

H O U G H T O N   M I F F L I N   C O M P A N Y   B O S T O N

Atlanta   Dallas   Geneva, Illinois   Palo Alto   Princeton   Toronto

Houghton Mifflin Edition, 1991

Printed in the U.S.A.
ISBN: 0–395–53891–2
BCDEFGHIJ–FL–99876543210

There were TEN in the bed

And the little one said,
"Roll over! Roll over!"
So they all rolled over
And one fell out . . .

There were NINE in the bed
And the little one said,
"Roll over! Roll over!"
So they all rolled over
And one fell out . . .

There were EIGHT in the bed
And the little one said,
"Roll over! Roll over!"
So they all rolled over
And one fell out . . .

There were SEVEN in the bed
And the little one said,
"Roll over! Roll over!"
So they all rolled over
And one fell out . . .

15

There were SIX in the bed
And the little one said,
"Roll over! Roll over!"
So they all rolled over
And one fell out . . .

There were FIVE in the bed
And the little one said,
"Roll over! Roll over!"
So they all rolled over
And one fell out . . .

There were FOUR in the bed
And the little one said,
"Roll over! Roll over!"
So they all rolled over
And one fell out . . .

There were THREE in the bed
And the little one said,
"Roll over! Roll over!"
So they all rolled over
And one fell out . . .

There were TWO in the bed
And the little one said,
"Roll over! Roll over!"
So they all rolled over
And one fell out . . .

25

There was ONE in the bed
And the little one said,
"I'm not getting up!"
The other NINE said,
"Oh, yes, you are!"

Then there were NONE in the bed
And no one said,
"Roll over! Roll over!"